The
Royal Horticultural Society
Diary 1998

*Paintings and drawings of fruit and flowers
from the Lindley Library*

Commentary by Brent Elliott

FRANCES LINCOLN

Frances Lincoln Limited
4 Torriano Mews
Torriano Avenue
London NW5 2RZ

The Royal Horticultural Society Diary 1998
Copyright © Frances Lincoln Limited 1997

All illustrations reproduced by courtesy of the Royal Horticultural Society

Illustrations copyright © The Royal Horticultural Society

Illustration of gooseberry 'Sheba Queen' by Augusta Innes Withers from *Treasures of the Royal Horticultural Society* by Brent Elliott, reproduced courtesy of The Herbert Press.

Astronomical information reproduced, with permission, from data supplied by HM Nautical Almanac Office, copyright © Particle Physics and Astronomy Research Council

British Library Cataloguing in Publication data
A catalogue record for this book is available from the British Library

ISBN 0 7112 1139 6
Typeset by Clive Dorman & Co.
Printed in Hong Kong

First Frances Lincoln edition: 1997

RHS FLOWER SHOWS 1998

All shows feature a wide range of floral exhibits staged by the nursery trade, with associated competitions reflecting seasonal changes, and horticultural sundries. With the exception of the shows at Malvern, Chelsea, Strathclyde, Birmingham, Hampton Court and Wisley, all RHS Flower Shows will be held in one or both of the Society's Horticultural Halls in Greycoat Street and Vincent Square, Westminster, London SW1.

These dates are correct at the time of going to press but before travelling to a Show we strongly advise you to check with the Diary Dates section of the RHS Journal The Garden, *or telephone the 24-hour Flower Show Information Line for the latest details. Tel: 0171 649 1885.*

EUROPEAN NATIONAL HOLIDAYS 1998
Holidays that fall on a Sunday are not included

AUSTRIA	Jan. 1, 6; April 13; May 1, 21; June 1, 11; Aug. 15; Oct. 26; Dec. 8, 25, 26
BELGIUM	Jan. 1; April 13; May 1, 21; June 1; July 11, 21; Aug. 15; Nov. 2, 11; Dec. 25, 26
DENMARK	Jan. 1; April 5, 9, 10, 13; May 8, 21; June 1, 5; Dec. 25, 26
FINLAND	Jan. 1, 6; April 10, 13; May 1, 21; June 20; Oct. 31; Dec. 25, 26
FRANCE	Jan. 1; April 13; May 1, 8, 21; June 1; July 14; Aug. 15; Nov. 11; Dec. 25
GERMANY	Jan. 1, 6; April 10, 13; May 1, 21; June 1, 11; Aug. 15; Oct. 3, 31; Dec. 25, 26
GREECE	Jan. 1, 6; March 2, 25; April 17, 20; May 1; June 8; Aug. 15; Oct. 28; Dec. 25, 26
ITALY	Jan. 1, 6; April 13, 25; May 1; Aug. 15; Dec. 8, 25, 26
LUXEMBOURG	Jan. 1; Feb. 23; April 13; May 1, 21; June 1, 23; Aug. 15; Sept. 7; Dec. 25, 26
NETHERLANDS	Jan. 1; April 10, 13, 30; May 5, 21; June 1; Dec. 25, 26
NORWAY	Jan. 1; April 9, 10, 13; May 1, 21; June 1; Dec. 25, 26
PORTUGAL	Jan. 1; April 10, 25; May 1; June 4, 10; Aug. 15; Oct. 5; Dec 1, 8, 25
SPAIN	Jan. 1, 6; March 19; April 9, 10; May 1; July 25; Aug. 15; Dec. 8, 25
SWEDEN	Jan. 1, 6; April 10, 13; May 1, 21; June 1, 20; Oct. 31; Dec. 25, 26
SWITZERLAND	Jan. 1; April 10, 13; May 1, 21; June 1; Aug. 1; Dec. 25, 26

Year Planner

1998

JANUARY
M	T	W	T	F	S	S
			1	2	3	4
5	6	7	8	9	10	11
12	13	14	15	16	17	18
19	20	21	22	23	24	25
26	27	28	29	30	31	

FEBRUARY
M	T	W	T	F	S	S
						1
2	3	4	5	6	7	8
9	10	11	12	13	14	15
16	17	18	19	20	21	22
23	24	25	26	27	28	

MARCH
M	T	W	T	F	S	S
						1
2	3	4	5	6	7	8
9	10	11	12	13	14	15
16	17	18	19	20	21	22
23	24	25	26	27	28	29
30	31					

APRIL
M	T	W	T	F	S	S
		1	2	3	4	5
6	7	8	9	10	11	12
13	14	15	16	17	18	19
20	21	22	23	24	25	26
27	28	29	30			

MAY
M	T	W	T	F	S	S
				1	2	3
4	5	6	7	8	9	10
11	12	13	14	15	16	17
18	19	20	21	22	23	24
25	26	27	28	29	30	31

JUNE
M	T	W	T	F	S	S
1	2	3	4	5	6	7
8	9	10	11	12	13	14
15	16	17	18	19	20	21
22	23	24	25	26	27	28
29	30					

JULY
M	T	W	T	F	S	S
		1	2	3	4	5
6	7	8	9	10	11	12
13	14	15	16	17	18	19
20	21	22	23	24	25	26
27	28	29	30	31		

AUGUST
M	T	W	T	F	S	S
					1	2
3	4	5	6	7	8	9
10	11	12	13	14	15	16
17	18	19	20	21	22	23
24	25	26	27	28	29	30
31						

SEPTEMBER
M	T	W	T	F	S	S
	1	2	3	4	5	6
7	8	9	10	11	12	13
14	15	16	17	18	19	20
21	22	23	24	25	26	27
28	29	30				

OCTOBER
M	T	W	T	F	S	S
			1	2	3	4
5	6	7	8	9	10	11
12	13	14	15	16	17	18
19	20	21	22	23	24	25
26	27	28	29	30	31	

NOVEMBER
M	T	W	T	F	S	S
						1
2	3	4	5	6	7	8
9	10	11	12	13	14	15
16	17	18	19	20	21	22
23	24	25	26	27	28	29
30						

DECEMBER
M	T	W	T	F	S	S
	1	2	3	4	5	6
7	8	9	10	11	12	13
14	15	16	17	18	19	20
21	22	23	24	25	26	27
28	29	30	31			

1999

JANUARY
M	T	W	T	F	S	S
				1	2	3
4	5	6	7	8	9	10
11	12	13	14	15	16	17
18	19	20	21	22	23	24
25	26	27	28	29	30	31

FEBRUARY
M	T	W	T	F	S	S
1	2	3	4	5	6	7
8	9	10	11	12	13	14
15	16	17	18	19	20	21
22	23	24	25	26	27	28

MARCH
M	T	W	T	F	S	S
1	2	3	4	5	6	7
8	9	10	11	12	13	14
15	16	17	18	19	20	21
22	23	24	25	26	27	28
29	30	31				

APRIL
M	T	W	T	F	S	S
			1	2	3	4
5	6	7	8	9	10	11
12	13	14	15	16	17	18
19	20	21	22	23	24	25
26	27	28	29	30		

MAY
M	T	W	T	F	S	S
					1	2
3	4	5	6	7	8	9
10	11	12	13	14	15	16
17	18	19	20	21	22	23
24	25	26	27	28	29	30
31						

JUNE
M	T	W	T	F	S	S
	1	2	3	4	5	6
7	8	9	10	11	12	13
14	15	16	17	18	19	20
21	22	23	24	25	26	27
28	29	30				

JULY
M	T	W	T	F	S	S
			1	2	3	4
5	6	7	8	9	10	11
12	13	14	15	16	17	18
19	20	21	22	23	24	25
26	27	28	29	30	31	

AUGUST
M	T	W	T	F	S	S
						1
2	3	4	5	6	7	8
9	10	11	12	13	14	15
16	17	18	19	20	21	22
23	24	25	26	27	28	29
30	31					

SEPTEMBER
M	T	W	T	F	S	S
		1	2	3	4	5
6	7	8	9	10	11	12
13	14	15	16	17	18	19
20	21	22	23	24	25	26
27	28	29	30			

OCTOBER
M	T	W	T	F	S	S
				1	2	3
4	5	6	7	8	9	10
11	12	13	14	15	16	17
18	19	20	21	22	23	24
25	26	27	28	29	30	31

NOVEMBER
M	T	W	T	F	S	S
1	2	3	4	5	6	7
8	9	10	11	12	13	14
15	16	17	18	19	20	21
22	23	24	25	26	27	28
29	30					

DECEMBER
M	T	W	T	F	S	S
		1	2	3	4	5
6	7	8	9	10	11	12
13	14	15	16	17	18	19
20	21	22	23	24	25	26
27	28	29	30	31		

29 *Monday*

30 *Tuesday*

31 *Wednesday*   JEWISH FESTIVAL OF CHANUKAH, EIGHTH DAY
                                  RAMADAN BEGINS (SUBJECT TO SIGHTING OF MOON)

1 *Thursday*   NEW YEAR'S DAY
                                        HOLIDAY, UK, REPUBLIC OF IRELAND,
                                  CANADA, USA, AUSTRALIA AND NEW ZEALAND

2 *Friday*   HOLIDAY, SCOTLAND AND NEW ZEALAND

3 *Saturday*

4 *Sunday*

A hand-coloured engraving of a grapefruit, Citrus × paradisi, *from Duhamel du Monceau's* Traité des arbres et arbustes *(1801-1825), after a drawing by Pancrace Bessa (1772-1830)*

*A watercolour drawing of an unnamed variety of auricula, known in
the early 19th century as a fringed or English auricula, by
Caroline Maria Applebee (fl. 1800s-1850s)*

5 *Monday*   FIRST QUARTER

6 *Tuesday*   EPIPHANY

7 *Wednesday*

8 *Thursday*

9 *Friday*

10 *Saturday*

11 *Sunday*

12 *Monday*   FULL MOON

13 *Tuesday*

14 *Wednesday*

15 *Thursday*

16 *Friday*

17 *Saturday*

18 *Sunday*

A chromolithograph of Lilium auratum *by Walter Hood Fitch (1817-1892) from*
A Monograph of the Genus Lilium *(1877-1880) by Henry John Elwes*

A hand-coloured engraving of the 'Monaco' fig from Giorgio Gallesio's
Pomona italiana *(1817-1839), after a drawing by Domenico del Pino (fl. 1820s)*

19 *Monday*   HOLIDAY, USA (MARTIN LUTHER KING'S BIRTHDAY)

20 *Tuesday*   LAST QUARTER   RHS FLOWER SHOW

21 *Wednesday*   RHS FLOWER SHOW

22 *Thursday*

23 *Friday*

24 *Saturday*

25 *Sunday*

26 *Monday*   HOLIDAY, AUSTRALIA (AUSTRALIA DAY)

27 *Tuesday*

28 *Wednesday*   NEW MOON   CHINESE NEW YEAR

29 *Thursday*

30 *Friday*

31 *Saturday*

1 *Sunday*

A chromolithograph of the orchid Odontoglossum laeve *by Walter Hood Fitch*
(1817-1892) from James Bateman's Monograph of Odontoglossum *(1874)*

A hand-coloured engraving of two species of crocus (Crocus banaticus *and* C. iridiflorus),
an unsigned plate published in Heinrich Gottlob Ludwig Reichenbach's
Icones florae Germanicae (1847)

2 *Monday*

3 *Tuesday*   FIRST QUARTER

4 *Wednesday*

5 *Thursday*

6 *Friday*   HOLIDAY, NEW ZEALAND

7 *Saturday*

8 *Sunday*

9   *Monday*

10   *Tuesday*

11   *Wednesday*   FULL MOON

12   *Thursday*   HOLIDAY, USA (LINCOLN'S BIRTHDAY)

13   *Friday*

14   *Saturday*   ST VALENTINE'S DAY

15   *Sunday*

A hand-coloured engraving of lychees (Litchi chinensis) *from the*
Transactions of the Horticultural Society *(1834), after a*
drawing by Miss S. A. Drake (fl. 1820s-1840s)

A chromolithograph of Anemone coccinea, *after a drawing by* C. Delorme (fl. 1870-1900), *from* Icones ad floram Europaeae (1866-1903) *by Alexis Jordan and Jules Pierre Fourreaux*

16 *Monday*   HOLIDAY, USA (WASHINGTON'S BIRTHDAY)

17 *Tuesday*   RHS FLOWER SHOW

18 *Wednesday*   RHS FLOWER SHOW

19 *Thursday*   LAST QUARTER

20 *Friday*

21 *Saturday*

22 *Sunday*

23 *Monday*

---

24 *Tuesday*   SHROVE TUESDAY

---

25 *Wednesday*   ASH WEDNESDAY

---

26 *Thursday*   NEW MOON

---

27 *Friday*

---

28 *Saturday*

---

1 *Sunday*   ST DAVID'S DAY, WALES

A watercolour drawing of a form of Iris pseudacorus *by Miss Williamson*
(fl. 1900s), made in 1905 from a specimen in the garden of
Ellen Willmott at Warley Place, Essex

A watercolour drawing of the passion flower Passiflora laurifolia, *made in Surinam
in the 1820s by John Henry Lance (1793-1878)*

2 *Monday*

3 *Tuesday*

4 *Wednesday*

5 *Thursday*   FIRST QUARTER

6 *Friday*

7 *Saturday*   LONDON ORCHID SHOW

8 *Sunday*   LONDON ORCHID SHOW

9   *Monday*   COMMONWEALTH DAY

---

10 *Tuesday*

---

11 *Wednesday*

---

12 *Thursday*

---

13 *Friday*   FULL MOON

---

14 *Saturday*

---

15 *Sunday*

A hand-coloured engraving of Pelargonium inquinans *from*
Duhamel du Monceau's Traité des arbres et arbustes *(1801-1825),*
after a drawing by Pancrace Bessa (1772-1830)

A watercolour drawing of the peony Paeonia clusii *by Lilian Snelling (1879-1972),
made for Sir Frederick Stern's* Study of the Genus Paeonia *(1946)*

16 *Monday*

17 *Tuesday*

ST PATRICK'S DAY, IRELAND
HOLIDAY, NORTHERN IRELAND AND REPUBLIC OF IRELAND
RHS FLOWER SHOW

18 *Wednesday*

RHS FLOWER SHOW

19 *Thursday*

20 *Friday*

VERNAL EQUINOX

21 *Saturday*   LAST QUARTER

22 *Sunday*

MOTHERING SUNDAY

23 *Monday*

24 *Tuesday*

25 *Wednesday*

26 *Thursday*

27 *Friday*

28 *Saturday*   NEW MOON

29 *Sunday*   BRITISH SUMMER TIME BEGINS (SUBJECT TO CONFIRMATION)

A hand-coloured engraving of strawberry 'Keen's Seedling' from
the Transactions of the Horticultural Society *(1822), after a drawing by*
Charles John Robertson (fl. 1820s)

A watercolour drawing of the daffodil 'The Doctor', made in 1913 by
Edward Augustus Bowles (1865-1954)

30 *Monday*

31 *Tuesday*

1 *Wednesday*

2 *Thursday*

3 *Friday*   FIRST QUARTER

4 *Saturday*

5 *Sunday*   PALM SUNDAY

6 *Monday*

7 *Tuesday*

8 *Wednesday*

9 *Thursday*   MAUNDY THURSDAY

10 *Friday*   GOOD FRIDAY

11 *Saturday*   FULL MOON   PASSOVER (PESACH) FIRST DAY

12 *Sunday*   EASTER SUNDAY

A *hand-coloured engraving of* Amaryllis (Sprekelia) formosissima,
after a drawing by Mrs Edward Bury (fl. 1820s-1860s), from her book A Selection
of Hexandrian Plants *(1831-1834)*

A watercolour drawing of black cherries, dated 1825,
by Augusta Innes Withers (1792-1869)

13 *Monday*   EASTER MONDAY

14 *Tuesday*   RHS FLOWER SHOW

15 *Wednesday*   RHS FLOWER SHOW

16 *Thursday*

17 *Friday*   PASSOVER (PESACH) SEVENTH DAY

18 *Saturday*   PASSOVER (PESACH) EIGHTH DAY

19 *Sunday*   LAST QUARTER

20　*Monday*

21　*Tuesday*　　　　　　　　　　　　　　　BIRTHDAY OF QUEEN ELIZABETH II

22　*Wednesday*

23　*Thursday*　　　　　　　　　　　　　　　ST GEORGE'S DAY, ENGLAND

24　*Friday*

25　*Saturday*　　　　　　　　HOLIDAY, AUSTRALIA AND NEW ZEALAND (ANZAC DAY)

26　*Sunday*　　　　NEW MOON

A hand-coloured engraving of a lilac, Syringa vulgaris, *from the* Flora Parisiensis
*(1808-1813) of Pierre Antoine Poiteau (1766-1859) and Pierre-Jean-François
Turpin (1775-1840), after a drawing by Turpin*

A *hand-coloured engraving of the pear 'Bon-chrétien d'Espagne' from*
Duhamel du Monceau's Traité des arbres fruitiers *(1807-1835), after a drawing*
by Pierre-Jean-François Turpin (1775-1840)

27 *Monday*

28 *Tuesday*   ISLAMIC NEW YEAR (SUBJECT TO SIGHTING OF MOON)
                                                              RHS FLOWER SHOW

29 *Wednesday*   RHS FLOWER SHOW

30 *Thursday*

1 *Friday*

2 *Saturday*

3 *Sunday*   FIRST QUARTER

4 *Monday*

MAY DAY HOLIDAY, UK (EXC. SCOTLAND) AND REPUBLIC OF IRELAND
SPRING HOLIDAY, SCOTLAND

5 *Tuesday*

6 *Wednesday*

7 *Thursday*

MALVERN SPRING GARDENING SHOW PREVIEW (TO BE CONFIRMED)

8 *Friday*

MALVERN SPRING GARDENING SHOW

9 *Saturday*

MALVERN SPRING GARDENING SHOW

10 *Sunday*

MOTHER'S DAY, CANADA AND USA
MALVERN SPRING GARDENING SHOW

A hand-coloured engraving representing the family Smilacaceae from Illustrations
of the Natural Orders of Plants *(1849-1855) by Elizabeth Twining
(1805-1889), after a drawing by the author*

A watercolour drawing of an iris of the Monspur group by Miss Williamson
(fl. 1900s), made in 1905 from a specimen in the garden of
Ellen Willmott at Warley Place, Essex

11 *Monday*   FULL MOON

12 *Tuesday*

13 *Wednesday*

14 *Thursday*

15 *Friday*

16 *Saturday*

17 *Sunday*

18 *Monday*   HOLIDAY, CANADA (VICTORIA DAY)

19 *Tuesday*   LAST QUARTER   CHELSEA FLOWER SHOW

20 *Wednesday*   CHELSEA FLOWER SHOW

21 *Thursday*   ASCENSION DAY
                                                                       CHELSEA FLOWER SHOW

22 *Friday*   CHELSEA FLOWER SHOW

23 *Saturday*

24 *Sunday*

A hand-coloured engraving of the poppy Papaver bracteatum, *after a drawing by* John Lindley (1799-1865), *from his* Collectanea botanica (1821)

*A hand-coloured engraving of the 'Trifera', or thrice-cropping grape,
from Giorgio Gallesio's* Pomona italiana *(1817-1839), after a drawing
by Isabella Bozzolini (fl. 1820s-1840s)*

25 *Monday*   NEW MOON   SPRING HOLIDAY, UK (EXC. SCOTLAND)
                                              MAY DAY HOLIDAY, SCOTLAND
                                              HOLIDAY, USA (MEMORIAL DAY)

26 *Tuesday*

27 *Wednesday*

28 *Thursday*

29 *Friday*   SCOTLAND'S NATIONAL GARDENING SHOW, STRATHCLYDE COUNTRY PARK

30 *Saturday*   SCOTLAND'S NATIONAL GARDENING SHOW, STRATHCLYDE COUNTRY PARK

31 *Sunday*   WHIT SUNDAY (PENTECOST)
                                        JEWISH FEAST OF WEEKS (SHAVUOT)
                              SCOTLAND'S NATIONAL GARDENING SHOW, STRATHCLYDE COUNTRY PARK

1 *Monday*

HOLIDAY, REPUBLIC OF IRELAND
HOLIDAY, NEW ZEALAND (QUEEN'S BIRTHDAY)

2 *Tuesday*

FIRST QUARTER

3 *Wednesday*

4 *Thursday*

5 *Friday*

6 *Saturday*

7 *Sunday*

TRINITY SUNDAY

An undated watercolour drawing of Rosa rugosa *by*
Edwin Dalton Smith (1800-c.1866)

A hand-coloured engraving of Digitalis ochroleuca, *after a drawing by John Lindley (1799-1865), from his* Digitalium monographia *(1821)*

8 *Monday*

9 *Tuesday*

10 *Wednesday*   FULL MOON   HOLIDAY, AUSTRALIA (QUEEN'S BIRTHDAY)
BBC GARDENER'S WORLD LIVE, BIRMINGHAM (TO BE CONFIRMED)

11 *Thursday*   CORPUS CHRISTI
BBC GARDENER'S WORLD LIVE, BIRMINGHAM (TO BE CONFIRMED)

12 *Friday*   BBC GARDENER'S WORLD LIVE, BIRMINGHAM (TO BE CONFIRMED)

13 *Saturday*   THE QUEEN'S OFFICIAL BIRTHDAY (SUBJECT TO CONFIRMATION)
BBC GARDENER'S WORLD LIVE, BIRMINGHAM (TO BE CONFIRMED)

14 *Sunday*   BBC GARDENER'S WORLD LIVE, BIRMINGHAM (TO BE CONFIRMED)

15 *Monday*

16 *Tuesday*

17 *Wednesday*   LAST QUARTER

18 *Thursday*

19 *Friday*

20 *Saturday*

21 *Sunday*

SUMMER SOLSTICE
FATHER'S DAY, UK, CANADA AND USA

A watercolour drawing of the gooseberry 'Champagne', drawn for the Horticultural Society in 1820 by Charles John Robertson

A hand-coloured engraving of Antirrhinum latifolium *from the* Flore
portugaise *(1800-1829) of Johann C. Hoffmannsegg and Friedrich Heinrich Link,
after a drawing by Gottfried Wilhelm Voelker (1775-1849)*

22 *Monday*

23 *Tuesday*   RHS FLOWER SHOW (TO BE CONFIRMED)

24 *Wednesday*   NEW MOON   RHS FLOWER SHOW (TO BE CONFIRMED)

25 *Thursday*

26 *Friday*

27 *Saturday*

28 *Sunday*

29 *Monday*

---

30 *Tuesday*

---

1 *Wednesday*   FIRST QUARTER   HOLIDAY, CANADA (CANADA DAY)

---

2 *Thursday*

---

3 *Friday*   HOLIDAY, USA (OBSERVED)

---

4 *Saturday*   INDEPENDENCE DAY, USA

---

5 *Sunday*

A *hand-coloured engraving of* Amaryllis crocata (*a variety, no longer extant, of*
Hippeastrum striatum), *after a drawing by Mrs Edward Bury* (fl. 1820s-1860s),
from her book A Selection of Hexandrian Plants (1831-1834)

A hand-coloured engraving of redcurrants from Duhamel du Monceau's
Traité des arbres fruitiers (1807-1835), *after a drawing by*
Pierre-Jean-François Turpin (1775-1840)

6   *Monday*

7   *Tuesday*   HAMPTON COURT PALACE FLOWER SHOW

8   *Wednesday*   HAMPTON COURT PALACE FLOWER SHOW

9   *Thursday*   FULL MOON   HAMPTON COURT PALACE FLOWER SHOW

10 *Friday*   HAMPTON COURT PALACE FLOWER SHOW

11 *Saturday*   HAMPTON COURT PALACE FLOWER SHOW

12 *Sunday*   HAMPTON COURT PALACE FLOWER SHOW
                                                                          BATTLE OF THE BOYNE

13 *Monday*   HOLIDAY, NORTHERN IRELAND

14 *Tuesday*

15 *Wednesday*   ST SWITHIN'S DAY

16 *Thursday*   LAST QUARTER

17 *Friday*

18 *Saturday*

19 *Sunday*

A chromolithograph of Dianthus egregius, *after a drawing
by C. Delorme* (fl. 1870-1900), *from* Icones ad floram Europaeae
(1866-1903) *by Alexis Jordan and Jules Pierre Fourreaux*

A hand-coloured engraving of three species of scabious, Scabiosa caucasica,
S. atropurpurea *and* S. graminifolia; *two of valerian,* Valeriana rubra *and* V. sibirica;
and Crucianella stylosa *(now* Phuopsis stylosa)*, from Jane Loudon's* Ladies'
Flower-Garden of Ornamental Perennials *(1849)*

20   *Monday*

21   *Tuesday*   RHS FLOWER SHOW

22   *Wednesday*   RHS FLOWER SHOW

23   *Thursday*   NEW MOON

24   *Friday*

25   *Saturday*

26   *Sunday*

27 *Monday*

28 *Tuesday*   WISLEY FLOWER SHOW (TO BE CONFIRMED)

29 *Wednesday*   WISLEY FLOWER SHOW (TO BE CONFIRMED)

30 *Thursday*   WISLEY FLOWER SHOW (TO BE CONFIRMED)

31 *Friday*   FIRST QUARTER

1 *Saturday*

2 *Sunday*

A hand-coloured engraving of the peach Prunus persica *from Duhamel du Monceau's* Traité des arbres et arbustes *(1801-1825), after a drawing by* Pancrace Bessa *(1772-1830)*

A watercolour drawing of an unnamed morning glory (Ipomoea *species*), *made in 1824 by John Curtis* (1791-1862)

3 *Monday*

SUMMER HOLIDAY, SCOTLAND
HOLIDAY, REPUBLIC OF IRELAND

4 *Tuesday*

5 *Wednesday*

6 *Thursday*

7 *Friday*

8 *Saturday*   FULL MOON

9 *Sunday*

10 *Monday*

11 *Tuesday*

12 *Wednesday*

13 *Thursday*

14 *Friday*   LAST QUARTER

15 *Saturday*

16 *Sunday*

A chromolithograph by Walter Hood Fitch (1817-1892) of two forms of
Lilium elegans *('Incomparabilis' and 'Alice Wilson'), from* A Monograph of the Genus
Lilium *(1877-1880) by Henry John Elwes*

*A hand-coloured engraving of the 'Abricot-pêche', or Nancy apricot, from
Duhamel du Monceau's* Traité des arbres fruitiers *(1807-1835), after a drawing
by Pierre-Jean-François Turpin (1775-1840)*

17 *Monday*

18 *Tuesday*   RHS FLOWER SHOW

19 *Wednesday*   RHS FLOWER SHOW

20 *Thursday*

21 *Friday*

22 *Saturday*   NEW MOON

23 *Sunday*

24　*Monday*

25　*Tuesday*

26　*Wednesday*

27　*Thursday*

28　*Friday*

29　*Saturday*

30　*Sunday*　　　FIRST QUARTER

A chromolithograph of Galatella oigoclada (*now included in* Aster), *after a drawing by C. Delorme* (fl. 1870-1900), *from* Icones ad floram Europaeae (1866-1903) *by Alexis Jordan and Jules Pierre Fourreaux.*

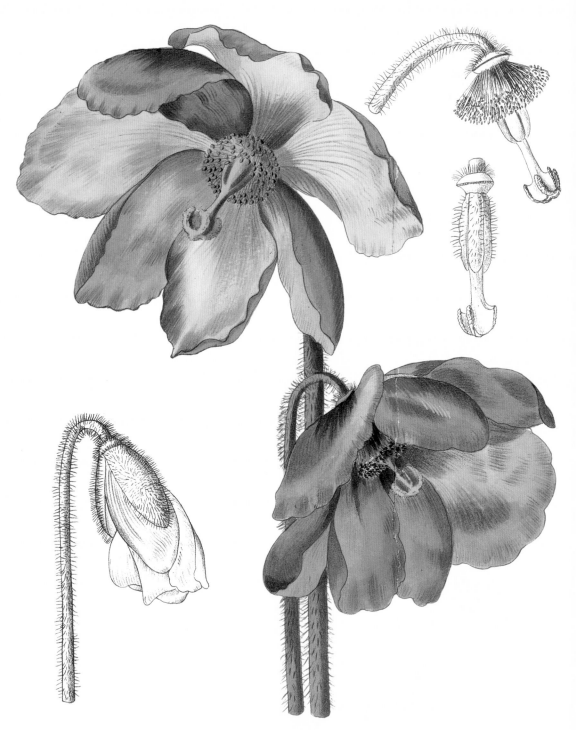

A *hand-coloured engraving of* Meconopsis grandis, *after a drawing by Lilian Snelling (1879-1972), published as plate 9304 of* Curtis's Botanical Magazine *(1933)*

31 Monday

1 Tuesday

2 Wednesday

3 Thursday

4 Friday

5 Saturday

6 Sunday FULL MOON

7 *Monday*   HOLIDAY, CANADA (LABOUR DAY) AND USA (LABOR DAY)

8 *Tuesday*

9 *Wednesday*

10 *Thursday*

11 *Friday*

12 *Saturday*

13 *Sunday*   LAST QUARTER

A watercolour drawing of the 'Norfolk Beaufin' apple, made in 1822 by Charles John Robertson (fl. 1820s)

A *hand-coloured engraving of* Verbascum blattaria *from the* Flore portugaise
(1800-1829) of Johann C. Hoffmannsegg and Heinrich Friedrich Link, after a drawing by
Gottfried Wilhelm Voelker (1775-1849)

14 Monday

15 Tuesday   RHS GREAT AUTUMN SHOW

16 Wednesday   RHS GREAT AUTUMN SHOW

17 Thursday

18 Friday

19 Saturday

20 Sunday   NEW MOON

21 *Monday*   JEWISH NEW YEAR (ROSH HASHANAH)

22 *Tuesday*

23 *Wednesday*   AUTUMNAL EQUINOX

24 *Thursday*

25 *Friday*

26 *Saturday*   MALVERN AUTUMN SHOW

27 *Sunday*   MALVERN AUTUMN SHOW

A chromolithograph of Lilium maximowiczii *by Walter Hood Fitch*
(1817-1892), from A Monograph of the Genus Lilium
(1877-1880) by Henry John Elwes

A hand-coloured engraving of the 'Early Orleans' plum from the
Transactions of the Horticultural Society *(1819), after a*
drawing by William Hooker (1779-1832)

28 *Monday*   FIRST QUARTER

29 *Tuesday*   MICHAELMAS DAY

30 *Wednesday*   JEWISH DAY OF ATONEMENT (YOM KIPPUR)

1 *Thursday*

2 *Friday*

3 *Saturday*

4 *Sunday*

5 *Monday*   FULL MOON   JEWISH FESTIVAL OF TABERNACLES (SUCCOTH) FIRST DAY

6 *Tuesday*   RHS FLOWER SHOW

7 *Wednesday*   RHS FLOWER SHOW

8 *Thursday*

9 *Friday*

10 *Saturday*

11 *Sunday*

A watercolour drawing of the wild cherry Prunus cerasus
by Dorothy Martin (1882-1949)

A hand-coloured engraving of Astrapaea (Dombeya) wallichii, *after a drawing by*
John Lindley (1799-1865), from his Collectanea botanica *(1821)*

12 *Monday*   LAST QUARTER   JEWISH FESTIVAL OF TABERNACLES (SUCCOTH) EIGHTH DAY
                                        HOLIDAY, CANADA (THANKSGIVING) AND USA (COLUMBUS DAY)

13 *Tuesday*

14 *Wednesday*

15 *Thursday*

16 *Friday*

17 *Saturday*

18 *Sunday*

19   *Monday*

20   *Tuesday*   NEW MOON

21   *Wednesday*

22   *Thursday*

23   *Friday*

24   *Saturday*   UNITED NATIONS DAY

25   *Sunday*   BRITISH SUMMER TIME ENDS (SUBJECT TO CONFIRMATION)

*A hand-coloured engraving of the 'Cannon Hall Muscat' grape from
the* Transactions of the Horticultural Society *(1832), after a
drawing by Augusta Innes Withers (1792-1869)*

A hand-coloured engraving of three species of rudbeckia, Rudbeckia columnaris,
R. pinnata *and* R. triloba, *together with* Telekia speciosa, Inula glandulosa, Silphium
trifoliatum *and* Chrysostemma *(now* Coreopsis*)* tripteris, *from Jane Loudon's*
Ladies' Flower-Garden of Ornamental Perennials *(1849)*

Week 44

October/November 1998

26 *Monday*
HOLIDAY, REPUBLIC OF IRELAND
HOLIDAY, NEW ZEALAND (LABOUR DAY)

27 *Tuesday*

28 *Wednesday*   FIRST QUARTER

29 *Thursday*

30 *Friday*

31 *Saturday*   HALLOWE'EN

1   *Sunday*   ALL SAINTS' DAY

2 *Monday* ,

---

3 *Tuesday*   RHS FLOWER SHOW

---

4 *Wednesday*   FULL MOON   RHS FLOWER SHOW

---

5 *Thursday*   GUY FAWKES' DAY

---

6 *Friday*

---

7 *Saturday*

---

8 *Sunday*   REMEMBRANCE SUNDAY

A drawing in Chinese colours by an anonymous artist of a form of tree peony or moutan, Paeonia suffruticosa, *sent to the Horticultural Society in the 1820s by John Reeves*

A hand-coloured engraving of forms of the common pear, Pyrus communis, *from Duhamel du Monceau's* Traité des arbres et arbustes *(1801-1825), after a drawing by Pancrace Bessa (1772-1830)*

9   *Monday*

---

10   *Tuesday*

---

11   *Wednesday*   LAST QUARTER   HOLIDAY, CANADA (REMEMBRANCE DAY) AND USA (VETERANS' DAY)

---

12   *Thursday*

---

13   *Friday*

---

14   *Saturday*

---

15   *Sunday*

---

16 *Monday*

17 *Tuesday*

18 *Wednesday*

19 *Thursday*   NEW MOON

20 *Friday*

21 *Saturday*

22 *Sunday*

A watercolour drawing of a double nasturtium, Tropaeolum majus, *from a manuscript entitled 'Flore de Désert', by an artist identified only by the initials A.E., made in the early years of the 19th century*

*A watercolour drawing by Sir Charles James Fox Bunbury (1809-1886) of a species
of lobelia observed in his South African travels in 1838*

23   *Monday*

---

24   *Tuesday*   RHS FLOWER SHOW

---

25   *Wednesday*   RHS FLOWER SHOW

---

26   *Thursday*   HOLIDAY, USA (THANKSGIVING DAY)

---

27   *Friday*   FIRST QUARTER

---

28   *Saturday*

---

29   *Sunday*   ADVENT SUNDAY

---

30 *Monday*   ST ANDREW'S DAY, SCOTLAND

1   *Tuesday*

2   *Wednesday*

3   *Thursday*   FULL MOON

4   *Friday*

5. *Saturday*

6   *Sunday*

A hand-coloured engraving of the apple 'Reinette Jaune Hâtive' from Duhamel du Monceau's Traité des arbres fruitiers *(1807-1835), after a drawing by Pierre-Jean-François Turpin (1775-1840)*

A hand-coloured engraving of Epidendrum vitellinum (Encyclia vitellina) *from John Lindley's* Sertum orchidaceum *(1838-1841), after a drawing by Miss S. A. Drake* (fl. 1820s-1840s)

7   *Monday*

8   *Tuesday*

9   *Wednesday*

10 *Thursday*   LAST QUARTER

11 *Friday*

12 *Saturday*

13 *Sunday*

14 *Monday*   JEWISH FESTIVAL OF CHANUKAH, FIRST DAY

15 *Tuesday*   RHS CHRISTMAS SHOW

16 *Wednesday*   RHS CHRISTMAS SHOW

17 *Thursday*

18 *Friday*   NEW MOON

19 *Saturday*

20 *Sunday*   RAMADAN BEGINS (SUBJECT TO SIGHTING OF MOON)

A *hand-coloured engraving of* Amaryllis carnavonia (*a variety of* Hippeastrum *no longer extant*) *from Augustin Pyramus de Candolle's* Plantes rares du Jardin de Genève (1829), *after a drawing by Jean Christophe Heyland (1791-1866)*

A hand-coloured engraving of a pomegranate, Punica granatum, *from* Duhamel du Monceau's Traité des arbres fruitiers *(1807-1835), after a drawing by* Pierre-Jean-François Turpin *(1775-1840)*

21 Monday   JEWISH FESTIVAL OF CHANUKAH, EIGHTH DAY

22 Tuesday   WINTER SOLSTICE

23 Wednesday

24 Thursday   CHRISTMAS EVE

25 Friday   CHRISTMAS DAY
HOLIDAY, UK, REPUBLIC OF IRELAND, CANADA, USA,
AUSTRALIA AND NEW ZEALAND

26 Saturday   FIRST QUARTER   BOXING DAY, ST STEPHEN'S DAY
HOLIDAY, UK, REPUBLIC OF IRELAND, CANADA,
AUSTRALIA AND NEW ZEALAND

27 Sunday

28 *Monday*   HOLIDAY, UK, REPUBLIC OF IRELAND AND NEW ZEALAND

29 *Tuesday*

30 *Wednesday*

31 *Thursday*

1 *Friday*   NEW YEAR'S DAY
                              HOLIDAY, UK, REPUBLIC OF IRELAND, CANADA, USA,
                                        AUSTRALIA AND NEW ZEALAND

2 *Saturday*   HOLIDAY, SCOTLAND

3 *Sunday*

A watercolour drawing of a chrysanthemum, Chrysanthemum indicum *or* Dendranthema indicum, *made in 1824 by John Curtis (1791-1862) and published as plate 2556 in the* Botanical Magazine

Biographies

Applebee, Caroline Maria (*fl.* 1800s-1850s) was an amateur artist whose surviving drawings, now in the Lindley Library, are dated between 1808 and 1852.

Bessa, Pancrace (1772-1830) was a pupil of Spaendonck and Redouté. Between 1810 and 1827, he produced 527 illustrations for a work entitled *Herbier général de l'amateur,* one of the most popular French illustrated works on garden plants, which exists in two editions with different texts. The drawings for this work were a gift from Charles X to the Duchesse de Berry, to whom Bessa had given painting lessons; she in turn left them to her sister, the Empress of Brazil; and in 1947 the collection was finally dispersed at auction. A few of the drawings are now in the Lindley Library.

Bowles, Edward Augustus (1865-1954) was the author of *My Garden in Spring, My Garden in Summer* and *My Garden in Autumn and Winter,* books which made famous his garden at Myddelton House, Enfield. He also wrote *A Handbook of Narcissus* and *A Handbook of Crocus and Colchicum.* He was for forty years chairman of the Royal Horticultural Society's Narcissus and Tulip Committee.

Bunbury, Sir Charles James Fox (1809-1886) collected plants in South Africa, South America, Madeira and the Canary Islands. The drawing illustrated here is taken from an album of drawings made on his African and South American travels in the 1830s, which is on permanent loan to the Royal Horticultural Society's Lindley Library.

Bury, Mrs Edward (*fl.* 1820s-1860s), née Priscilla Susan Falkner, was a botanical artist based in Liverpool. Her major work was a book entitled *A Selection of Hexandrian Plants* (1831-1834), for which she drew her own plates. 'Hexandrian' means plants with six anthers in Linnaeus' system of classification, then still popular in England.

Bozzolini, Isabella (*fl.* 1820s-1840s) was an Italian artist known primarily as an illustrator of Giorgio Gallesio's *Pomona italiana* (1817-1839), the greatest Italian fruit book.

Curtis, John (1791-1862), born in Norwich, worked as an engraver for the Horticultural Society's *Transactions* before becoming principal artist for the *Botanical Magazine,* for which he made over 400 illustrations by 1832. He is remembered primarily as an entomologist, although his multi-volume *British Entomology* (1824-1839) includes illustrations of plants as well as insects.

Delorme, C. (*fl.* 1870-1900) was the principal illustrator for Alexis Jordan and Jules Pierre Fourreau's *Icones ad floram Europae* (1866-1903), the major illustrated work on European plants in the latter half of the 19th century.

Drake, Miss S. A. (*fl.* 1820s-1840s) is believed to have been a relative of John Lindley's wife. Lindley employed her as the principal illustrator for his magazine *The Botanical Register;* she also collaborated with Mrs Withers on the plates for James Bateman's massive *Orchidaceae of Mexico and Guatemala* (1837-1843).

Fitch, Walter Hood (1817-1892) made over 2700 plates for Curtis's *Botanical Magazine* from 1834 to 1877, as well as illustrations for *Icones Plantarum,* Hooker's *Rhododendrons of Sikkim-Himalaya,* and Elwes' *A Monograph of the Genus Lilium.*

He produced so much work that his reputation for facility came to be held against him, but his drawings always illustrated the accompanying description with great accuracy.

Heyland, Jean Christophe (1792-1866) began his career as a barber in Frankfurt am Main. By the 1820s he was being employed as an artist by Augustin Pyramus de Candolle, Director of the Geneva Botanic Garden, and later became the Botanic Garden's principal botanical artist.

Hooker, William (1779-1832) was a pupil of Franz Bauer. His first important commission was the plates for R. A. Salisbury's *Paradisus Londinensis* (1805-1808); Salisbury was a founder member of the Horticultural Society, which hired Hooker in 1815 as its first artist. He is best known for the fruit drawings he made for the society, and for his *Pomona Londinensis.* In 1822, however, he stopped painting, probably as the result of a stroke. He is commemorated in the colour name 'Hooker green'.

Lance, John Henry (1793-1878), after whom the orchid *Oncidium lanceanum* is named, was a Commissary Judge in Surinam from 1828 to 1834. An amateur botanist, while living in Surinam he painted orchids and other exotic plants.

Lindley, John (1799-1865) was Assistant Secretary of the Horticultural Society for most of his career, during which time he also edited the *Botanical Register* and the *Gardeners' Chronicle,* laid the foundations of modern orchidology, served as Professor of Botany at University College and wrote a score of books. It was his library, purchased by the Horticultural Society in 1866, which formed the nucleus of the present Lindley Library. Nonetheless, he was first employed by the Society as an artist and drew the plates for his first books himself.

Loudon, Jane Wells (1807-1858), née Webb, attracted the attention of her future husband, John Claudius Loudon, by her science-fiction novel, *The Mummy* (1827). She published a large number of books on botany and gardening, most notably *Gardening for Ladies* (1840). The artists of the plates for her illustrated books on annuals, perennials, greenhouse plants and British wild flowers have never been identified.

Martin, Dorothy (1882-1949) was art mistress at Roedean School from 1916 to 1949. She exhibited occasionally over the years, but concentrated her effort on a projected British flora, which she never completed. She found her specimens in the Sussex countryside, and in the Lake District, where the school was evacuated during the Second World War.

Pino, Domenico del (fl. 1820s) was an Italian artist, known primarily as an illustrator of Giorgio Gallesio's *Pomona italiana* (1817-1839), the greatest Italian fruit book.

Robertson, Charles John (fl. 1820s) was hired by the Horticultural Society in 1820 to succeed William Hooker on his retirement. Nothing is known about Robertson's life and career apart from the 28 drawings of fruits in the Hooker series, made between 1820 and 1825.

Smith, Edwin Dalton (1800-c.1866) flourished from the 1820s to the 1840s; nothing is known about his early life. Among the works he illustrated were Maund's *Botanic Garden* and several books by the nurseryman Robert Sweet about florists' and garden flowers. He also drew roses and chrysanthemums for the Horticultural Society.

Snelling, Lilian (1879-1972) began her career under the patronage of the arboriculturist H. J. Elwes (a former patron of W. H. Fitch), drawing plants at his garden at Colesbourne in Gloucestershire. From 1916 to 1921 she worked at the Edinburgh Botanic Garden, and from 1922 to 1952 she illustrated Curtis's *Botanical Magazine,* as well as Sir Frederick Stern's *Study of the Genus Paeonia* and the *Supplement to Elwes' Monograph of the Genus Lilium.* She was awarded the Victoria Medal of Honour in 1955.

Turpin, Pierre-Jean-François (1775-1840) was one of the most important and prolific botanical artists of his time. Among the works which he illustrated were the 'Nouveau Duhamel' (*Traité des arbres fruitiers,* 1807-1835), Humboldt and Bonpland's *Voyage aux régions equinoctiales* and Chaumeton's *Flore médicale.* For this last work Turpin and his collaborator Poiret wrote a supplement entitled *Leçons de flore,* which was separately published in 1820; in this Turpin showed himself to be an original botanist as well as an artist.

Twining, Elizabeth Mary (1805-1889), a member of the famous family of tea merchants, was an amateur botanist of good standing and the author of works on botany for schools. Her major work was *Illustrations of the Natural Orders of Plants,* published in two volumes in 1849-1855, with a second edition in 1868.

Voelker, Gottfried Wilhelm (1775-1849) was a painter of designs on porcelain, hired by the Austrian botanists Johann von Hoffmannsegg and Heinrich Friedrich Link to draw the plates for their massive *Flore portugaise* in 1809. After 1820 cutbacks in funds reduced the number of plates and the quality of their printing, but the plates in the first volume in particular are of the highest quality and have been unjustly neglected.

Williamson, Miss (fl. 1900s) has not been conclusively identified; she might be Ella Williamson, whose address during the Edwardian period was given as Paris, but who exhibited at the Society of Women Artists in London. The pictures reproduced here are taken from an album of 35 coloured drawings of irises, made for Ellen Willmott during the years 1904-1908, apparently from varieties flowering in her garden at Warley Place, near Brentwood in Essex. The garden fell into dereliction after Willmott's death in 1934 and is now maintained as a country park.

Withers, Augusta Innes (1792-1869), née Baker, began her career working for the Horticultural Society in the 1820s. In 1830 she was appointed flower painter to Queen Adelaide, and later became Flower and Fruit Painter in Ordinary to Queen Victoria.

FRONT COVER
A chromolithograph of Lilium speciosum *by Walter Hood Fitch (1817-1892) from* A Monograph of the Genus Lilium *(1877-1880) by Henry John Elwes*

TITLE PAGE
A watercolour drawing of gooseberry 'Sheba Queen', drawn for the Horticultural Society in 1825 by Augusta Innes Withers (1792-1869)

BACK COVER
A hand-coloured illustration of different types of fruit and flower structure by Pierre-Jean-François Turpin (1775-1840) from Leçons de flore *(1819-1820) by Turpin and Jean-Louis-Marie Poiret*